Usborne

Little Coloring
Things That Go

Illustrated by Jenny Brown

Words by Kirsteen Robson

A plane flies high.

A car goes on roads.

A steam engine
puffs.

A rocket zooms.

A boat sails on water.

A bus is big.

A garbage truck collects trash.

A digger
scoops dirt.

A motorcycle is noisy.

A helicopter hovers.

A truck carries things.

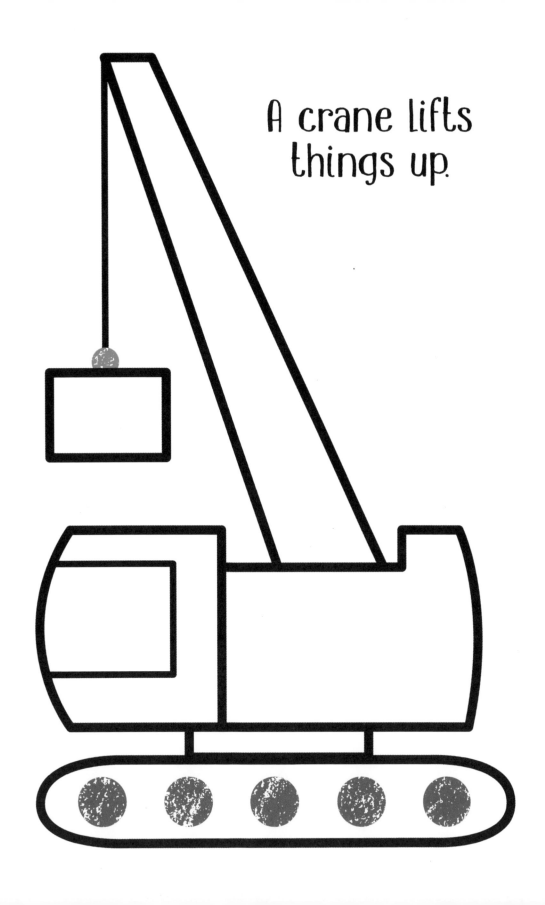

A crane lifts
things up.

Race cars
go very fast.

A ferry chugs
slowly.

A van hurries along.

A roller-coaster
rides on rails.

A balloon
drifts.

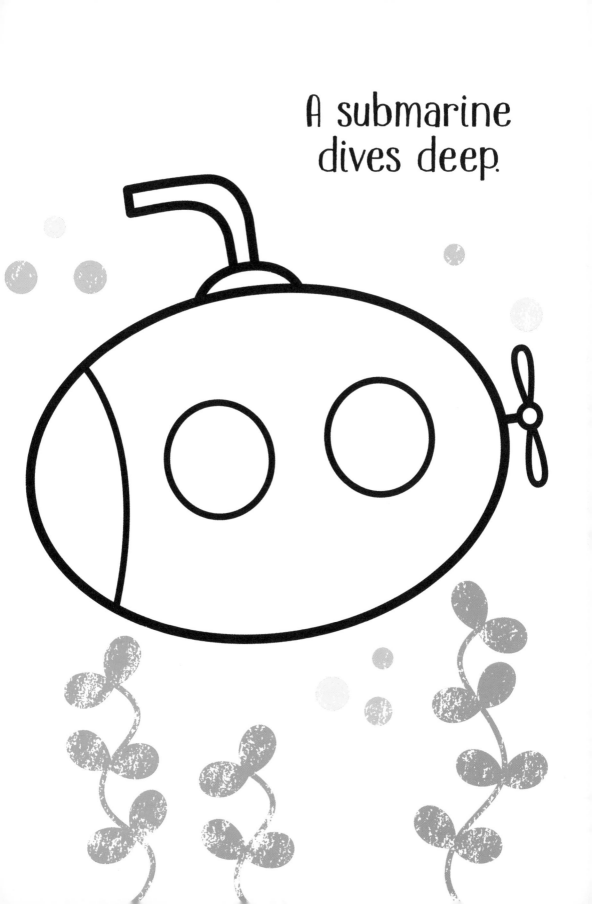

A submarine
dives deep.

A tractor in mud

A seaplane landing

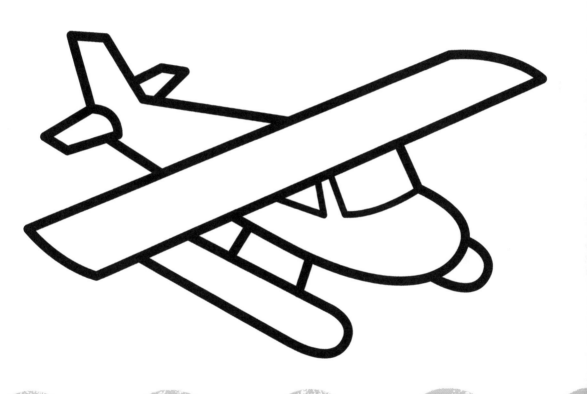

A fire truck wails.

A forklift beeps.

A go-kart whizzes
around a track.

A tram connects to electric wires.

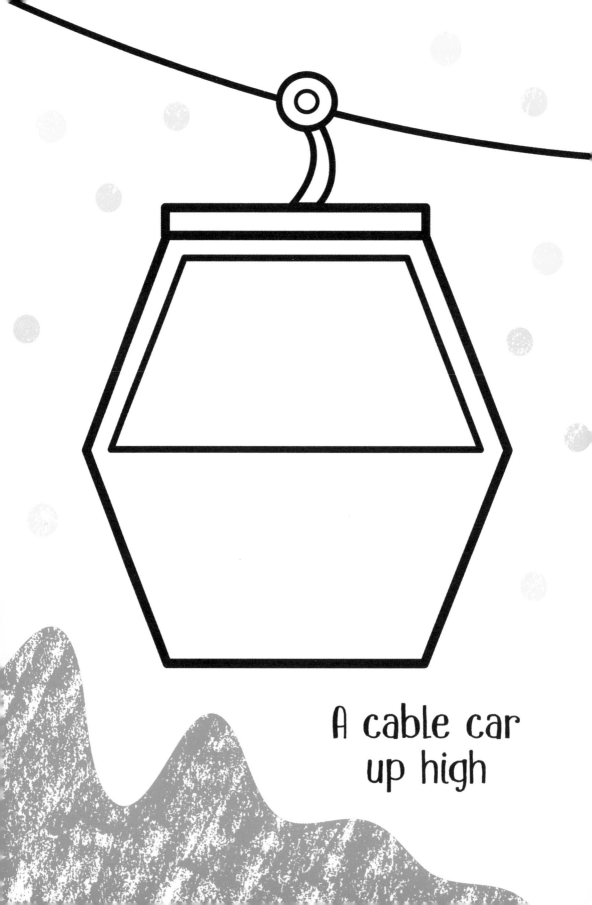

A cable car
up high

A motor home
on grass

A tow truck and
broken-down car

A fishing boat at sea

Trains go through tunnels.

A dump truck
carries dirt.

A parachute
floats down.